Founded
in
1888

+
598.1
M13b

Cop. 4

Date Due

SUPERIOR PUBLIC LIBRARY
SUPERIOR, WISCONSIN

BRODART   PRINTED IN U.S.A.

23-264-002

BUZZTAIL

THE STORY OF
A RATTLESNAKE

written and illustrated by

Robert M. McClung

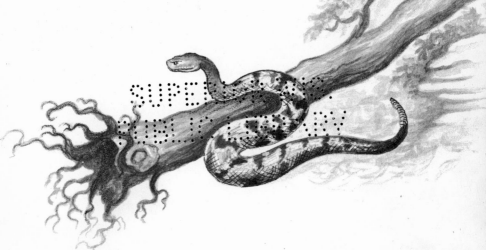

WILLIAM MORROW AND COMPANY
NEW YORK 1958

cop. 4

598.1
M13b

SUPERIOR WIS.

The author wishes to thank Dr. James A. Oliver,
Curator of Reptiles of the New York Zoological Park,
for reading and criticizing the manuscript.

© 1958 by Robert M. McClung. All rights reserved. Published
simultaneously in the Dominion of Canada by George J. McLeod
Limited, Toronto. Printed in the United States of America.
Library of Congress Catalog Card No. 58-5142

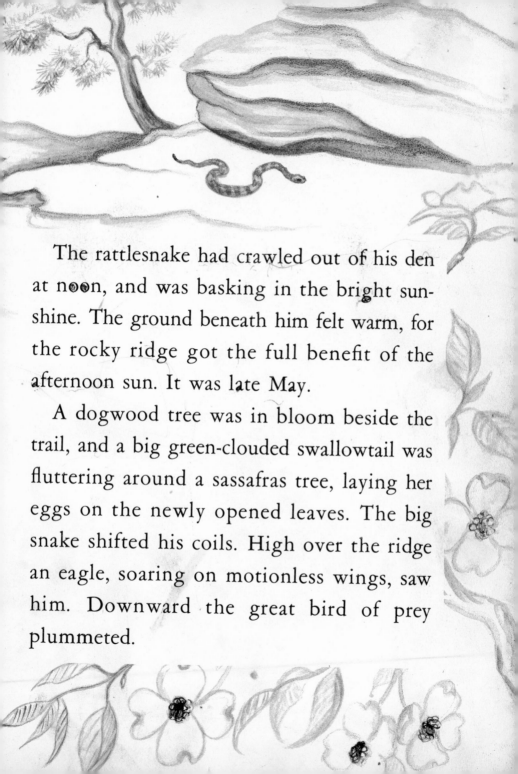

The rattlesnake had crawled out of his den at noon, and was basking in the bright sunshine. The ground beneath him felt warm, for the rocky ridge got the full benefit of the afternoon sun. It was late May.

A dogwood tree was in bloom beside the trail, and a big green-clouded swallowtail was fluttering around a sassafras tree, laying her eggs on the newly opened leaves. The big snake shifted his coils. High over the ridge an eagle, soaring on motionless wings, saw him. Downward the great bird of prey plummeted.

The eagle attacked quickly, its sharp talons grasping the snake's middle. Surprised, the snake struck back, and his fangs just grazed the tip of one of the eagle's rapidly beating wings.

For a split second the eagle relaxed its grip. Before it could seize the snake again, he had glided under a big overhanging rock. Bobbing its head, the eagle peered under the rock for a moment. Then it flapped heavily away.

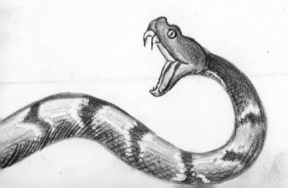

It was not until the next day that the snake crawled out again, and lay at full length in the sun. Buzztail was nearly six feet long—a giant among timber rattlesnakes. His body was as thick around as a man's arm, and he weighed seven pounds. He was an old snake and had lived near this same den for twelve years.

His smooth, elastic skin was covered with scales. On his back and sides they were arranged in uniform rows; and each scale was diamond-shaped, with a ridge, or keel, down its center. On his flat belly were wide scales called scutes, each of which overlapped the one behind it. Buzztail's scales formed definite patterns of different colors. His background color was a dull yellowish-brown, with many dark, sooty crossbands.

His head was broad and flat, with a blunt snout. His round, pale yellow eyes had vertical pupils in them, as cats' eyes have. They were covered by transparent, immovable eyelids.

At the other end of him were the rattles that gave Buzztail his name. There were fourteen segments, or individual rattles, in all. In his lifetime he had had many more than these, but some of them had broken off. That did not matter, though, for Buzztail got a new rattle every time he shed his skin.

The sun rose higher in the sky and warmed Buzztail. As is the case with all cold-blooded animals, his body heat changed with the temperature of his surroundings. He could not maintain a constant temperature the way warm-blooded animals—mammals and birds—do. He felt restive in the warm air, and started to crawl across the rocks and through a patch of low huckleberry bushes.

Buzztail had no legs, but he was able to move along very well without them. He glided ahead, pulling his belly scutes forward in successive sections by muscle action, and then drawing up the rest of his body behind them. He wasn't in a hurry today, but when he was, his whole body squirmed from side to side, forming S-shaped curves. The outer sides of the curves pressed against rough spots in the ground, pushing him forward. After crawling slowly through the underbrush, Buzztail coiled up among some dead leaves.

A dull booming noise started nearby. It was made by a male ruffed grouse, drumming to attract a mate. Time after time the cock repeated his booming, with wings quivering, feathers ruffled, and tail spread.

A sleek brown female grouse hopped onto a rock close to Buzztail. She was intent on the male's drumming and did not see the snake. Buzztail waited for her to come closer.

She walked slowly through the leaves, scratching a bit as though looking for food. The male drummed again, and the hen cocked her head to listen. She was just five feet away from Buzztail. He waited, motionless as a statue—waited for his meal to come a couple of feet closer.

Suddenly a chipmunk flashed out of a
hole under a nearby rock. Startled, the hen
grouse took off with a whir of wings. The

chipmunk skittered first one way and then another, its little brush tail sticking straight up in the air. It sat up on its haunches to eat a seed, then scampered closer to Buzztail. He was watching the chipmunk closely, for his eyes could see movement as much as fifteen feet away. Soon it would be near enough for him to strike.

The chipmunk saw Buzztail and dashed away with a shrill cry of terror. Snakes cannot hypnotize or charm their prey, but occasionally an animal may become so frightened by a snake that for a moment it cannot move. The chipmunk had not been *that* scared, however!

Buzztail crawled a short distance away and settled down for another wait. Something else would come along.

Every so often, as he waited, Buzztail flicked his tongue out through a notch in his upper lip. His tongue was forked and dark colored, with black tips on each fork. It was not a "stinger," as some people call it, but an organ for touching. It helped Buzztail to taste and smell the things around him.

Every time his tongue flicked out, the tips picked up tiny particles from the air, or from whatever they touched, and carried them back to two small cavities in the roof of his mouth. Nerve endings in these cavities made it possible for him to taste or smell whatever his tongue brought in. Buzztail also used his nostrils for smelling, as well as for breathing.

Buzztail had no external ears and could not even hear his own rattles when he vibrated them. He could feel vibrations through the ground, however.

Between Buzztail's nostrils and eyes there were two pits, or holes. These had nerve endings in them that were sensitive to small differences in temperature. They reacted to the heat coming from the bodies of warm-blooded animals, such as the grouse and the chipmunk, and carried the message to his brain. In this way Buzztail could tell where his prey was, even when he couldn't see it.

Snakes with pits like these are called pit vipers. All rattlesnakes have pits. So do their relatives, the poisonous copperhead and the water moccasin.

The sun sank low in the western sky, and dark shadows stretched up the slope. A young wood rat, too hungry to wait for darkness to come, crept out of its nearby nest and along the rock ledge. It came closer and closer to Buzztail, its long whiskers quivering. It did not see the rattler until it was too late.

Buzztail struck from his coiled position, lunging forward three feet, or half the length of his body. His jaws opened wide as his head shot forward, and his three-quarter-inch-long fangs stabbed the luckless wood rat. He withdrew quickly and re-coiled, waiting. He did not need to strike again.

The wood rat ran several feet before it keeled over. It kicked convulsively several times and then lay still. It was dead. The rattlesnake venom had taken its effect.

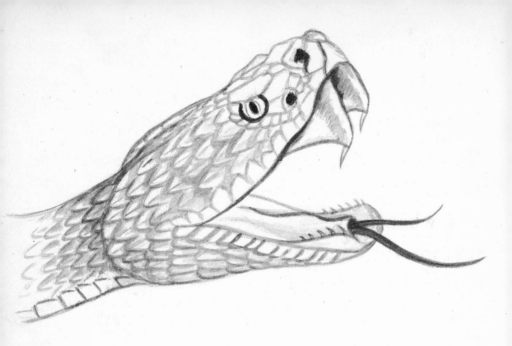

Buzztail's venom was stored in two sacs, similar to salivary glands, that were located inside his cheeks, behind the eyes. A narrow tube connected each gland with a long, hollow fang on either side of the roof of his mouth. When Buzztail struck, strong muscles squeezed venom out of the gland, through the fang, and into the wound. The fang worked like a hypodermic needle.

The fangs were anchored in hinged bones which could rotate backward and forward. When Buzztail's mouth was closed, the fangs folded back against the roof of his mouth. But when he opened his jaws, the fangs sprang into an upright position, ready for biting. Behind each of the fangs in use were several partly developed ones, ready to take the place of either regular fang if it was broken off or pulled out.

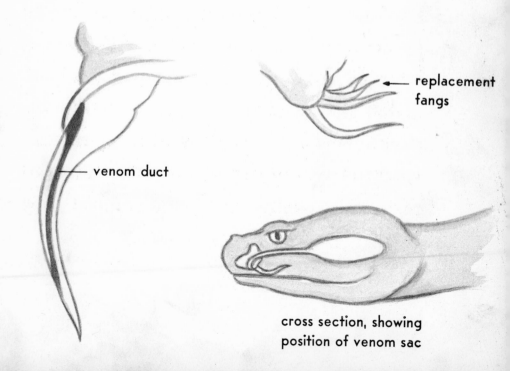

venom duct

replacement fangs

cross section, showing position of venom sac

Buzztail crawled over to the dead wood rat and touched it with his tongue. Then he seized it in his jaws and began to swallow it. Snakes do not chew their food; they swallow it whole. Eating the wood rat was a long, slow process, for the wood rat's body was thicker than Buzztail's head.

Taking a firm grip with his backward-curving teeth, Buzztail pushed one side of his upper jaw forward on the rat's head as far as it would go, and clamped his teeth down. He did the same with the other side of his upper jaw, and then, in turn, with the two halves of his lower jaw. The halves of each of Buzztail's jaws were connected by

strong, flexible ligaments which allowed each section to stretch apart and work separately. This arrangement, plus his elastic skin, made it possible for him to swallow animals whose bodies were bigger around than his.

Little by little the wood rat disappeared. Its body became coated with saliva as it went down, making it easier for Buzztail to swallow. Finally only its tail could be seen. That soon disappeared too.

Buzztail crawled back under the rock and lay at full length. There was a big bulge in his middle where the wood rat was, and he was very lethargic. For three days he lay there, digesting his meal.

Later, as he crawled back toward the rocky ledge, his flicking tongue picked up the scent of a female rattlesnake. The odor excited Buzztail, and he followed the trail. It was mating time.

Just ahead of him, a doe ambled out of the scrub, followed by a spotted fawn. The doe did not see Buzztail, but the fawn did. It stepped toward him, sniffing curiously.

Buzztail gathered his body into coils and began to rattle a warning. Then the doe saw him and came over at a run. Butting the fawn aside, she headed straight for Buzztail.

Stopping short, she jumped into the air, and her two pairs of sharp hoofs drove down at Buzztail's head. He reared back, and the attack missed him by inches. He, in turn, lunged at the doe, and she shied away.

Before she could jump at him again, Buzztail had glided under a rock, away from danger. The doe snorted and stamped her feet defiantly. Then she and the fawn disappeared into the brush. Soon Buzztail came out and followed the trail of the female snake again.

Something else moved in front of him. It was a big male rattler. Buzztail reared his head at this new threat and exhaled, hissing loudly. The rival, almost as big as Buzztail, was a dull black color all over, with bands of an even deeper black showing faintly. The black rattler raised its head as it came toward Buzztail. It hissed too. The two snakes faced each other, their heads swaying high above the ground. The black male advanced slowly.

Buzztail lunged forward and struck the other male with his head, knocking him backward. The next moment their bodies were thrashing on the ground, as each attempted to throw his coils about the other.

Again and again Buzztail tried to tighten his coils around the other snake, but the black male twisted and turned every time, avoiding him. They reared against each other, Buzztail's head and neck parallel with those of the other snake. Each repeatedly tried to knock the other off balance. Neither attempted to bite, however, and for all their struggling, neither one hurt the other. At last the black male disentangled himself and slithered off into the underbrush.

Buzztail promptly turned back to the trail of the female. Following it, he came to a big rock near the den. There was the female rattlesnake, sunning herself.

Buzztail glided up beside her and rubbed his chin along her back. They flicked their tongues over each other, getting acquainted. The female was about four feet long, and much lighter and brighter than Buzztail was. She was a sulphur-yellow color, with pale tan crossbands.

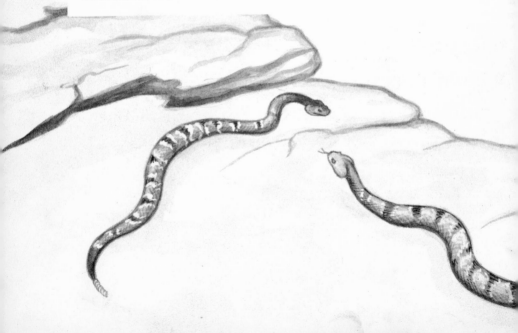

A fat porcupine clambered awkwardly
down a nearby pine tree and waddled by, but
neither snake paid any attention to it. Buzztail courted the female rattler for some time
before they mated. That evening he left her
and crawled away by himself.

For some days Buzztail's eyelids had been milky, and his skin dry and flaky. Repeatedly he rubbed his head on rocks and rough bark. Finally the skin around his mouth loosened. Rubbing still more, he pushed the tissue-paper-thin layer of skin back across his upper jaws and over his eyes. The skin on his lower jaws peeled back too. Then, slithering through the underbrush and against stones and roots, he crawled slowly out of his skin. It lay behind him like an empty glove turned inside out. All the ticks, mites, and other parasites that had burrowed between the scales in his old skin were left behind too.

Buzztail's new skin was much brighter and fresher-looking than the old one. It was cool and dry, and not at all moist or slimy. Now Buzztail had one more rattle than before. It had been forming under the old skin and had come into view when the skin was shed.

June passed into July, and the weather became very warm and dry. The summer sun made the rocks so hot that Buzztail could not stand them for more than a few minutes at a time. He took to resting under the shady ledge during the day, coming out only in the early morning or evening. It had not rained for some weeks, and the tiny springs below the rocky ridge gradually dried up. One evening Buzztail started down the mountainside toward the broad valley below.

Far down the rocky slopes, with their scrub growth of oak and sassafras, he crawled. Then he went through an open forest of tall hemlocks, where mountain laurel and rhododendron grew beneath the trees. Beyond the forest was a sloping meadow, where a tiny brook gurgled through the tall grass. A frightened rabbit bounded away as Buzztail glided over to the stream and thrust his nose into the water. He took a long drink. He did not lap with his tongue, but sucked in the water, his throat muscles working steadily as he swallowed.

When he had finished he crawled on through the tall grass. A pale moon bathed the countryside in silver, and the trees ahead cast faint shadows on the ground.

On the other side of the trees was a wide asphalt road. The asphalt, still warm from the sun, felt good on Buzztail's belly as he started across. He stopped for a moment to rest, and felt a vibration. Ahead, speeding toward him, were two big blinding eyes.

They roared over him, one on either side, stirring up a whirlpool of wind that knocked him sprawling. A car had gone over him.

Buzztail slithered quickly off the road. He had been fortunate to escape. Many animals are killed by speeding cars.

Going on, he approached a cluster of farm buildings. The sun was peeping above the horizon, and a rooster crowed. Buzztail crawled under a rock by the corner of an old weathered barn. There he stayed until late that afternoon.

When he ventured out he saw a herd of cows coming up the lane toward him. Behind them were a boy and his dog. Buzztail coiled into his defensive position and shook his rattles vigorously as the dog dashed in to attack him.

Buzztail struck out, but the dog, yelping with excitement, danced back out of reach. Buzztail re-coiled immediately as the dog came at him again.

The boy called the dog away. Stooping, he picked up a stick and rushed toward Buzztail. The boy knew that most snakes are beneficial, for they prey on rats and other rodents that do damage to crops. But he did not want any rattlesnakes around the farm, because their poisonous bite makes them too dangerous to have nearby.

Seizing the dog by the scruff of the neck, the boy pushed him aside and aimed a blow at Buzztail's head with his stick. But the excited dog got in his way again, and the boy had to stop and push him away once more.

Seizing the opportunity, Buzztail escaped by crawling into a crack in the stone fence beside the lane. At dusk he came out and went on. Soon he came to a wide creek, running dark and silent between tree-lined banks. Slithering down the bank, Buzztail thrust his nose into the water and drank.

Nearby was a big buck. He was drinking too, his velvety antlers almost touching the water. Suddenly aware of the rattlesnake, the buck snorted, then started toward him. Buzztail slipped into the water and swam to the other side. He did not go into the water often, but he was a good swimmer.

Buzztail stayed near the creek for some weeks. He took over an abandoned skunk hole under an old stump for his headquarters. During the heat of the day he usually stayed inside the burrow or coiled up at its entrance. He did most of his roaming either at dusk or in the early morning hours.

There were lots of other reptiles near the creek. Nearly every day garter snakes passed the stump, hunting for frogs or toads, which are their main food.

One day a female pilot black snake laid twenty-three white eggs in the rotting wood under part of the stump. Each egg was over an inch in length and had a tough leathery shell.

Another time a painted turtle came out of the creek to dig a hole in the soft ground with her hind legs. She laid her eggs in the hole, and then filled it in again. She smoothed the spot over so other animals could not find the eggs.

Buzztail was dozing under the log one afternoon when he felt vibrations above him. The stump was moving. Suddenly a landslide of dirt fell in on him. Buzztail crawled quickly out of the burrow. There, almost on top of him, was a big black bear. It had been digging under the stump, searching for grubs and field mice.

Hissing loudly, Buzztail vibrated the tip of his tail as fast as he could. The rattles shook back and forth as often as fifty times a second. They made a high, droning noise, like the noise a cicada makes—or an electric buzzer. The bear woofed in surprise. Then it turned tail and lumbered away. It wanted no part of Buzztail!

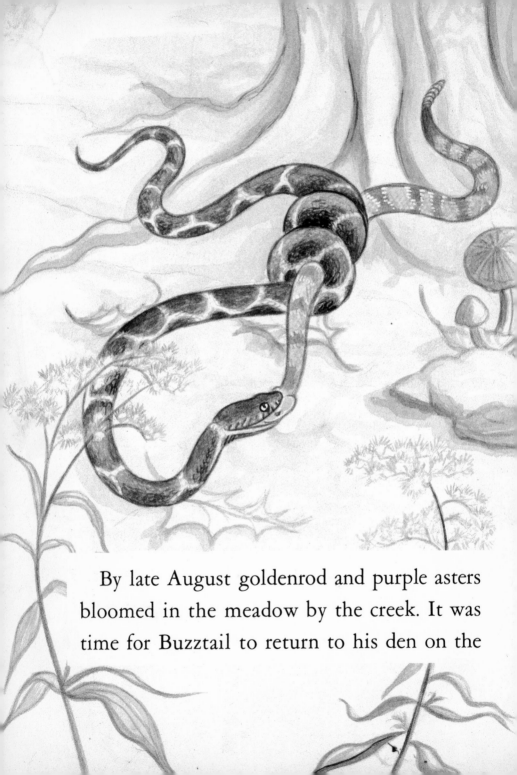

By late August goldenrod and purple asters bloomed in the meadow by the creek. It was time for Buzztail to return to his den on the mountainside. On his way back he came upon a big king snake that was holding a smaller rattler in its coils. It had just started to swallow the rattlesnake. King snakes eat all kinds of other snakes, and sometimes swallow rattlers as big as they are. Their victims may bite them, but king snakes are immune to rattlesnake venom. Buzztail went on, and soon he was back at the rocky ridge near the top of the mountainside. A number of other rattlers were there too.

One morning while he was basking in the sunshine by the den, the yellow female he had mated with that spring came and stretched out at full length near him. She looked thick and lumpy, and moved slowly. She started to twist and turn, as though she was trying to force something out.

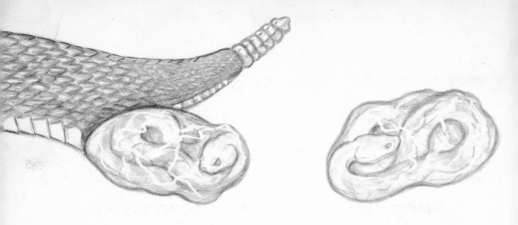

At last a soft, transparent capsule came out of her vent. It was about the size of a ping-pong ball, but so soft and quivery that it changed shape on the ground. Inside it was a baby rattlesnake, wriggling about and pushing its head against the membrane. In a few moments the membrane broke, and the little snake crawled out. Rattlesnakes do not lay eggs, the way black snakes do. Their young develop inside the mother's body until they are ready to be born.

The baby rattlesnake resembled its parents, but was only ten inches long. It looked around and flicked out its tongue, examining this new world it had just entered. Then it crawled over to a sunny spot near Buzztail and lay still.

During the next several hours, sixteen other little rattlesnakes were born. All of them came into the world fully equipped to take care of themselves. They were able to crawl about, catch prey, and inflict poisonous bites, just as Buzztail could. It was lucky for them that they were able to take care of themselves, for their parents paid no attention to them at all.

prebutton   button   button and first segm

At birth, each rattlesnake has a tiny node, called a pre-button, at the end of its tail. When it is a few days old, the baby rattler sheds its skin and gets a button—the first segment of its rattle. From then on it gains a segment every time it sheds. Each new rattle grows inside the previous one, and is loosely interlocked with it.

During their first year, timber rattlers shed their skin four or five times and grow to be eighteen or twenty inches long. At two years, they measure twenty-four inches or more, and when they are three, over thirty inches. By this time they have as many as ten or eleven rattles, and are grown up enough to have young of their own. After that they grow more slowly, and usually shed only once a year.

cross section of rattle, showing how segments are joined

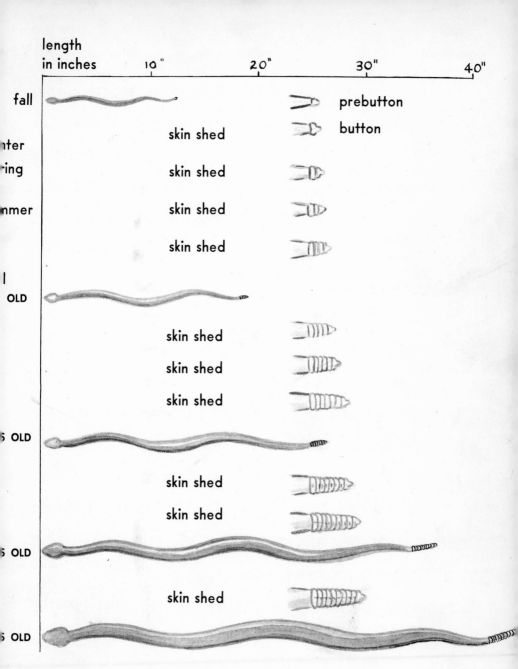

average growth rate of a timber rattlesnake

In late September the nights became chilly, and the days were cool too. Many rattlers had gathered along the ridge, ready to retire into the dens when the real cold came. Now Buzz-tail spent most of the time deep under the sheltering rocks, and came out only when the weather was warm.

In the second week of October, the weather suddenly became hot again. Sassafras and birch leaves gleamed golden in the sunshine, and sumac and dogwood flamed crimson on the slopes. High above the ridge, the migrating hawks and eagles were like tiny specks in the sky. Fallen leaves rustled on the ground, and the air carried the faint, pleasant smell of distant wood smoke. It was Indian summer.

Buzztail and the other snakes came out of their dens in great numbers, to bask in the warm sunshine. One afternoon the woods below them rang with shouts, as a party of men came up the trail from the valley. The men knew the snakes would be out sunning themselves in the mild weather. They had come up to kill them.

SUPERIOR WIS
PUBLIC LIBRARY

cop. 4

When the men were almost upon them, the snakes took alarm and started to scatter in all directions. Advancing, the men began to strike the snakes with sticks, clubs, and all sorts of other weapons. They killed every rattler in sight, as well as a few nonpoisonous snakes that were there. Man is the greatest enemy rattlesnakes—or any snakes—have.

A few of the snakes escaped by crawling into the dens. Others coiled in defense and struck at their attackers, but the men killed them before they could bite. When they had killed all the snakes they could find, the men went away. Buzztail was safe, for he had retreated into a deep crack in the rock ledge.

The next afternoon the boy who had seen Buzztail on his farm that summer came up the trail to the snake dens. He had heard about the snake-killing party and was curious to see the dead snakes.

He wandered about for a while, poking at the dead snakes with a stick. He did not see Buzztail, who was sunning himself beside a log. Without looking, the boy climbed carelessly over the log and stepped right on Buzztail's rattle.

Startled, the big rattlesnake struck out. His long fangs pierced the boy's trousers and buried themselves in his leg, just below the knee. Then, withdrawing quickly, Buzztail crawled back out of sight in his den.

After his first cry of surprise, the boy hurried away from the rock ledge and sat down in a little cleared area below it. He was frightened as he looked at the two fang marks, for he knew how serious a rattlesnake bite could be. Already there was a fierce throbbing in his leg. He grimaced, feeling the pain shooting up his leg like fire. The leg was becoming swollen and discolored.

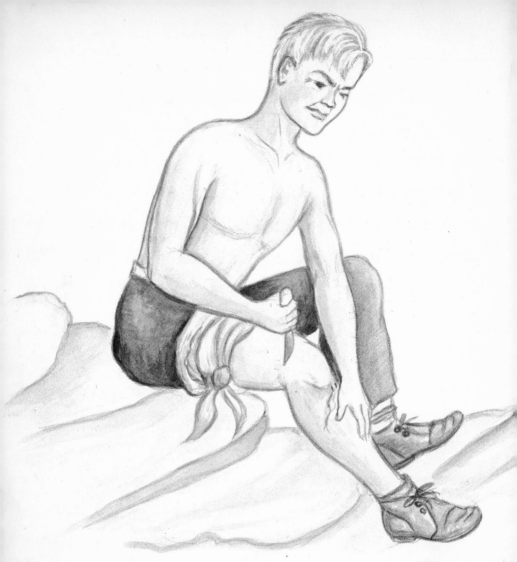

Quickly he took off his shirt and twisted
it tightly around his thigh to make a tourniquet. Then he took out his pocketknife and

sterilized the blade with a match. Gritting his teeth, he pressed down with the blade and made several lengthwise cuts, each about a half an inch long and a quarter of an inch deep, over each fang mark. He knew it was important to remove as much venom as possible. Rattlesnake venom affects the blood. It destroys red corpuscles and tiny blood vessels. He bent down and sucked at the cuts, spitting out blood and venom.

The pain from the bite made the boy feel dizzy, but doggedly he kept up the emergency treatment. After fifteen minutes he loosened the tourniquet for a few moments, so the circulation would not be completely cut off. He did not know how he was going to get down the mountainside. He knew he couldn't make it alone.

A half hour later two hunters found him. They carried him down the trail to their car, and rushed him to the nearest hospital. There the doctors gave him antivenin to counteract the rattlesnake venom. Antivenin is a serum taken from the blood of horses that have been injected repeatedly with increasingly large doses of rattlesnake venom until they have developed an immunity to it. Their blood manufactures antibodies which combat or neutralize the venom.

The boy recovered from Buzztail's bite, but it was many days before he was completely well again. He didn't blame Buzztail, though. He knew it was his own fault that he had been bitten.

Meanwhile, Buzztail was snug in his den on the mountainside. The day after he had

bitten the boy the weather turned cold, and there was a severe frost. Some of the young rattlesnakes froze to death. They had crawled under a log, and were not sheltered enough from the cold.

Buzztail was safe, though. He crawled back into a deep crack between the rocks until he came to a small compartment, six feet underground and fifteen feet away from the den entrance. A number of other rattlesnakes were there too, as well as several copperheads and a pilot black snake.

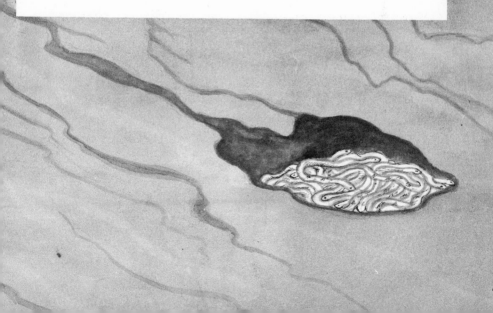

Outside it became colder and colder. Ice and snow soon sealed the entrance to the den. During the winter the temperature on the mountainside went down to zero and below at times, but in the underground compartment it remained fairly constant at several degrees above freezing. Buzztail and the other snakes twined together and became torpid and inert. Their breathing and other body activities slowed down drastically. All winter they stayed that way, motionless and cold. They looked dead. They were not dead, though. They were hibernating—sleeping through the cold winter.

When spring came, with its warm rains and rising temperatures, the snakes began to stir. One warm sunny day in early May, Buzztail crawled sluggishly to the den entrance and lay for a few moments in the sunshine. As the days became warmer, he and the other snakes spent more time outside.

One afternoon a big bobcat found Buzztail. Bobcats do not often attack rattlesnakes, but this one did.

He sprang at Buzztail and then jumped
back, playing with him as a house cat plays
with a mouse. Buzztail struck back, and his
fangs brushed against the other animal's fur.
The big cat circled, then dashed in to the
attack once more. He lashed out with his paw,
and his sharp talons ripped bloody furrows in
Buzztail's back. Buzztail struck back a second
time, but the bobcat leaped out of reach as

before. He was very quick. Again his long claws slashed deep cuts in Buzztail's body. Buzztail tried repeatedly to retreat to the shelter of the den, but every time he uncoiled to crawl away, the bobcat dashed in and clawed him. Unless he got away soon, the bobcat would kill him.

Coiling, striking, slithering forward bit by bit, Buzztail at last made his way into a corner of rock where he was protected on two sides.

SUPERIOR WIS.
PUBLIC LIBRARY

Now he could defend himself properly. Rattling furiously, he coiled and struck out at the animal. The bobcat leaped away, then stood spitting and snarling, his ears laid back, his nose wrinkled in anger. He knew that the odds were against him now. With a final scream of defiance he bounded away.

Buzztail let out a loud hiss, and then settled back. Gradually his rattling subsided. He rested his head on the rim of his coils and looked out over the slope. He was still the biggest rattler on the mountainside— ready to take on whatever came along.